First published 2012 by Macmillan Children's Books
a division of Macmillan Publishers Limited
20 New Wharf Road, London N1 9RR
Basingstoke and Oxford
Associated companies throughout the world
www.panmacmillan.com

ISBN 978-1-4472-0530-2

Written by Rachel Elliot

1 3 5 7 9 8 6 4 2

A CIP catalogue record for this book is available from
the British Library.

Printed and bound in Europe

Alert! Alert!
Lab's Critter Contraption has gone berserk!
It's on the rampage around the Binscape,
making critters left right and centre.
Can Tink and Clott find the machine and the critters
before the Bin is trashed?
One thing's for certain: they're going to need your help!

LAB'S CRITTER CONTRAPTION

The machine rampages through the Binscape, making critters wherever it goes.
Gam calls all the Secret Weevil Service agents to Castle Gam.
'Someone has to stop this confounded Critter Contraption!' he shouts.

Draw Castle Gam's dragon flying here.

Add a scared Bin Weevil.

Construct an SWS secret agent kit.

All the agents gather around the SWS table.
'Someone has to round up these critters,' says Tink. 'I volunteer me and Clott.'
'WHAT?' shrieks Clott.

The screens around the room start to flash.
'Problem in the Rum's Airport sector,' says Gam.
'We'll investigate!' says Tink.

Who is skulking in the shadows?

Finish drawing Gam.

Here's Lab with his head in his hands. What was he thinking?

What is this Bin Weevil doing?

Flem Manor's puzzles are in a mess.
Questions and answers are scattered everywhere, and letters and words are upside down and backwards.
'The critter's swinging from the chandelier!' squeals a blue Bin Weevil.

Tink and Clott build a tower of tables and chairs.
They lasso the critter with a long lead.
Now, where has that Critter Contraption gone?

The Beetle Critter is lurking here.

What is this Bin Weevil shouting?

Complete this puzzle:
Name an animal with a trunk!

Who's slipping on this banana skin?

There are more missing letters down here.

What does a critter made of banana skins look like?

Wobbletastic! Draw Tink and Clott's furniture tower.

Tink and Clott arrive at Dosh's Palace with the critters.
'The Bin Weevil Changer is in overdrive!' shouts Dosh.
'The new critter is inside the machine and it's meddling with the controls! It's changing the colours and shapes of all the Bin Weevils in the Palace.

'Charge! The Banana Skin Critter gallops towards the critter in the machine. Hurray! It slips on a banana skin and lands on the OFF switch.
But the Critter Contraption has disappeared again . . .

Stylish!
Give Dosh a
Tycoon-worthy
top hat.

Draw the control panel here.

Squirt!
Show the critter being zapped by Tink.

Finish the net off so it's ready to catch the critter.

It's heading for the Multiplex!

At Tink's Tree, something is scrabbling around in the branches.
'The machine is making critters in my tree!' wails Tink.
Tink and Clott climb up the tree. A critter is dangling from a nearby branch.

The critter is made of scraps and waste food. It smells really bad!
Gotcha! Clott captures the critter in his net and turns it into a Bin Pet.

At Rigg's Multiplex, a GINORMOUS pink-and-green critter wearing 3-D glasses is taking up fifteen seats.
'Help!' yells Tink as the critter pelts them with popcorn.

Uh-oh! The zapper is jammed up with popcorn!
Clott does a jig in front of the screen to distract the critter while Tink unblocks the zapper.
SHAZAM! Tink turns the critter into a Bin Pet.

Tink and Clott follow the trail to Club Fling.
Critters of all shapes and sizes are
jamming to the beat.
'The dance floor is packed!' beams Fling,
striking a pose.

Bin Fever!

CLUB FLI

Draw Fling's favourite dance pose here.

Draw a dancing critter here.

The Critter Contraption has stopped outside the Shopping Mall!
Lab meets Tink and Clott there.
He's carrying a large spanner and a very clever book.

Tink and Clott back the machine into a dark corner.
Meanwhile the Bin Weevils in the Mall have noticed the Bin Pets.
'They're so cute!'
'I want one!'
'This one looks just like me!'

What is this Bin Weevil saying?

Oh no! This Venus flytrap is trying to bite a Bin Pet!

Draw the Bin Pets arriving at the Shopping Mall.

Tink and Clott's Bin Pet Shop is the busiest store in the Mall.
'What shall we call it?' ponders Clott.
The Bin Pet Maker sits in the corner, churning out Bin Pets.

There's just one teeny-weeny little problem . . .
Lab keeps thinking up new ways to tinker with the machine!
What will he make it do next?

What's for sale on this shelf?

What is Lab's latest invention idea?

Draw a Bin Pet poster here.

Give the new shop a name.

Draw the Bin Pet Maker.

Pet Mulch

Draw a very rare Bin Pet.

Draw a crowd of customers waiting to go in.

Look out for more Bin Weevils titles to add to your collection!

ISBN 978-1-4472-0534-0

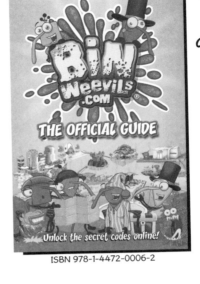

ISBN 978-1-4472-0006-2

ISBN 978-1-4472-0003-1

ISBN 978-1-4472-0004-8

Create your own Bin Weevil now at
www.binweevils.com

BACKWARDS BONUS!
Hold this page up to a mirror to reveal a secret code,
then enter it into the Mystery Code Machine at Lab's Lab
to collect a BIN-tastic nest item!

9865LD3271